My First Acrostic

The North

Edited by Lisa Adlam

First published in Great Britain in 2010 by:

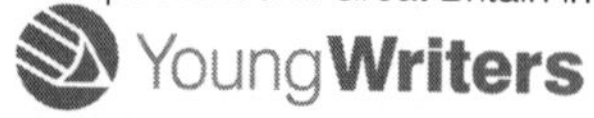

Young Writers
Remus House
Coltsfoot Drive
Peterborough
PE2 9JX
Telephone: 01733 890066
Website: www.youngwriters.co.uk

SB ISBN 978-1-84924-849-5

Foreword

The 'My First Acrostic' collection was developed by Young Writers specifically for Key Stage 1 children. The poetic form is simple, fun and gives the young poet a guideline to shape their ideas, yet at the same time leaves room for their imagination and creativity to begin to blossom.

Due to the young age of the entrants we have enjoyed rewarding their effort by including as many of the poems as possible. Our hope is that seeing their work in print will encourage the children to grow and develop their writing skills to become our poets of tomorrow.

Young Writers has been publishing children's poetry for over 19 years. Our aim is to nurture creativity in our children and young adults, to give them an interest in poetry and an outlet to express themselves. This latest collection will act as a milestone for the young poets and one that will be enjoyable to revisit again and again.

Contents

Amble Links First School, Amble Morpeth
Lee Brown (6)........ 1
Brandon Thompson (5)........ 1
Georgia Schroeder (6)........ 2
Michael Alan Brown (6)........ 2
Ella Henderson (6)........ 2
Charlie Yates (6)........ 3
Joanne Dawson (5)........ 3
Shane Nelson-Henderson (6)........ 3
Kieran Hume (6)........ 4
Nathan Charlton (7)........ 4
Shauna Carruthers (7)........ 4
Tyler Charlton (5)........ 5
Neeve Jamieson (6)........ 5
Bobby Stone (5)........ 5
Lewis Fairbairn (6)........ 6
Emily Fairbairn (6)........ 6
Adam Moyle (6)........ 6
Sian Moyle (6)........ 7
Evan Jukes (5)........ 7

Barlows Primary School, Liverpool
Conor Doran (6)........ 7
Emily Brooksbank (6)........ 8
Sam Cass (6)........ 8
Harry Brierley (6)........ 9
Maya Jones (6)........ 9
Lucy Beaumont (6)........ 10
Ben Bentley (6)........ 10
Mia Wheeler (6)........ 11
Jak Lydiate (6)........ 11
Ella Conway (6)........ 12
Emma Jones (6)........ 12
Eva Warbis (6)........ 13
Matthew McDonald (6)........ 13
Joshua Bond-Readle (6)........ 14
Oliwia Jankowska (6)........ 14
Callum Walthew (6)........ 14
Daniel Grierson (6)........ 15
Daniel Philip Snape (6)........ 15
Joshua Clark Newsome (6)........ 15
Nicola Ravenscroft (6)........ 16
Lewis Doran (6)........ 16
Megan Dickson (6)........ 16
Grace Faulkner (5)........ 17
Molly Garside (6)........ 17
Luke Evans (6)........ 17

Bowker Vale Primary School, Crumpsall
Solomon Asante-Owusu (6)........ 18
Momina Butt (7)........ 18
Humariaa Butt (6)........ 19
Megyn Betty Leon (6)........ 19
Akashraj Singh (6)........ 20
Sana Kayani (6)........ 20
Sami Ahmad (6)........ 20

Cambois First School, Cambois
Charlie Cox (6)........ 21
Billie Law (6)........ 21
Jacob-Russan Pritchett (6)........ 21
Jennie Butcher (6)........ 22
Kieran Elliott (6)........ 22

Castle Park School, Kendal
Ruben Baron (6)........ 22
Daisy Schwarzer (6)........ 23
Luke Tamblin (6)........ 23
Paige Hogg (6)........ 24
Jessika Foulds (6)........ 24
Theo Alderson (6)........ 25
Leah Rylands (6)........ 25
Matilda Hall (6)........ 26
Scott Wilkinson (6)........ 26
Mia Jones (6)........ 27
Abbie Barwise (7)........ 27
Kyle Needham (6)........ 28
Cody Haines (6)........ 28
Fraser Owen Donaldson (6)........ 28
Jacob Dixon (6)........ 29
Nathaniel Key (6)........ 29
Andrew Kneale (6)........ 29
Dylan Beagan (6)........ 30
Scott James Darnborough (6)........ 30
Jack Rigg (6)........ 30

Rhys Wright (6) 31
Alfie Burrow (6) 31
Sophie Kissock (6) 31
Ellie Kennah (6) 32
Connor Jackson (6) 32
Zachary Canwell (6) 32
Denis Morar (6) 33
Lauren Slater (6) 33
Ryan Blayney (6) 33
Alex Bland (6) 34
Nicole Leadbitter (6) 34

Christ Church Primary School, Wirral

Millie Wilson (7) 34
Ellie Boultbee (6) 35
Kiera Payne (6) 35
Chloe Hayward (6) 35
Katie Taylor (6) 36

Ghyllside Primary School, Kendal

Ben Weston 36
Isla Norman (6) 36
Angus Corrie 37
Grace Anastasie Cooke (6) 37
Daniel Betoin 37
Dylan Hill (6) 38
Kate Slater (7) 38
Phoebe Rudd (6) 38
Elizabeth Johnson 39
Lucy Greener (6) 39
Josh Smith (7) 39

Heron Hill Primary School, Kendal

Caitlin Whitehead (7) 40
Sophie Butler 40
Xander Armstrong 41
Rebecca Dyer 41
Lottie Beardwood 42
Michael Wilson 42
Gabriella Parker 43
Hannah Elvey 43
Caitlin Coombes 44
Tia Foley (6) 44
Maddy Tidman (6) 45
Isabel Toms 45
Sam Jones (6) 46
Joshua Irving (6) 46
Amy Woodhouse (6) 47
Millie Stephens (6) 47
Tia Leather 47
Amy Dugdale (6) 48
Louisa Dand (6) 48
Chloe Nileh O'Connor (6) 48
Ellie May 49
Luey Machell (6) 49
Mason Wilson (6) 49
Danusia Pantechis (7) 50
Charlotte Dixon (7) 50
Calum Morgan (6) 50
Miya Burrow 51
Marc Milburn 51
Jake Edwards (6) 51
Ben Mercer (6) 52

Lamplugh CE School, Frizington

Matthew Blacklock (6) 52
Eleanor Saville (6) 53
Joe Cusack (7) 53
Ben Shepherd (6) 54
Bob Price (6) 54

Manchester Muslim Preparatory School, Withington

Sameer Munir (6) 55
Hannah Safiyya Awah (6) 55
Umar Jamaal Din (5) 55
Hasan Bham (6) 56
Adlan Anazim (6) 56
Isaam F Akhtar (6) 56

Mount Primary School, Wallasey

Casey Burton (6) 57
Dominic Bell (7) 57
Freya Rivett (6) 57
Rebecca Anne Louise Stuffins (6) 58
Grace Myers (7) 58
Heidi Slater (6) 58
Chloe Pybis Crowley (5) 59
Rachel Foster (6) 59
Emily Murray (6) 59
Katie Allen (6) 60
Clara Satherley (6) 60
William Joy (6) 60
Ellie Jo-Anne Moore (6) 61
Amy Dunderdale (6) 61

Bradley Guy (6) 61
Luke Foulkes (7) 62
Owen Radcliffe (7) 62
Ben Newton (6) 62

Parish CE Primary School, St Helens

Austin Mathison (7) 63
Danny Foster (7) 63
Jack Martin (6) 63

St Edmund's RC Primary School, Manchester

Tyreeze Cunliffe (6) 64
Joseph Mannion (6) 64
Nancy Makaita Maziwisa (6) 64
Joseph Hegarty (6) 65
Emily Crotty (6) 65
Katie Heslop (6) 65
Abigail Jeffreys (6) 66
Imani Kolade-Newell (6) 66
Cade Serrette (6) 66
Joshua Harris (7) 67
Jack Field (7) 67

St Gregory's Catholic Primary School, Workington

Zoe Carter (6) 67
Hannah Rose Smith (5) 68
Alfie McDonald (7) 68
Demi-Lee McCann (5) 69
Ashleigh Murphy (6) 69
Jessica Humes (5) 70
Jack Swinburne (6) 70
Kodie Kirkwood (6) 71
Ciaran O'Donnell (6) 71
Bailey Shaw (6) 72
Lauren Bateman (6) 72
Aimee Graham (6) 73
Josh Cunningham (6) 73
Tayla-Jaye Humphreys (5) 73
Corben Shaw (5) 74
Joshua Lillico (5) 74
Molly Davies (6) 74

St John's CE Primary School, Darlington

Charlotte Anderson
& Nattaliya Sehman (6) 75
Joshua Brannan (6) 75
Joel Towers (7) 75
Sam White (6) 76
Oliver Pattinson (6) 76
Kayleigh Midgley (6) 76
Ellie White (6) 77
Harry Doyle (6) 77
Jack Wheelhouse (6) 77
Rebecca Hastie (6) 78
Sinead Johnstone (6)
& Demi-Lee Wilson (7) 78
Chloe Sperring (6) 78
Holly Cowley (6) 79
Mia Wall (6) 79
Matthew Plimmer (6) 79

St Joseph's RC Primary School, Coundon

Emily Addison (5) 80
Ruth Alderson (5) 80
Laura Askew-Wells (5) 80
Kai Wheatley (5) 81
Kerandeep Randhawa (5) 81
Meera Marley (5) 81
Alannah Burns (6) 82
Sam Bewick (5) 82

St Michael's RC Primary School, Houghton-le-Spring

Elliott Barry (6) 82
Connor James Lavelle (6) 83
Luke Sinton Robson (7) 83
Emma Bowater (6) 84
Olivia Lish (6) 84
Bradley McCarthy (6) 85
May Turner (6) 85
Thomas Weetman (6) 86
Taylor Bowe (7) 86
Chloe Chapman (6) 87
Isaac Lulham (6) 87
Harry John Huitson (6) 88
Bethany-Louise Burnhope (7) 88
Venna Brumby (6) 89

Emily Robinson (6) 89
Matthew Robinson (6) 89
Alexander Winter (7) 90
Charlie McLeod (6) 90
Lily Masters (6) 90
Chloe Brice (6) 91
Annabelle Napier (6) 91
Sophia Robson (6) 91

Star of the Sea RC Primary School, Whitley Bay

Ellie Macciocchi (6) 92
William Gray (6) 92
Mark Archer R Arquintillo (6) 93
Matthew Duffy (7) 93
Carlo Redpath (6) 94
Ely S Medina (6) 94
Erin Caulfield (6) 95
Molly Rudd (6) 95
Josiel Martin (6) 96
Jude Raynor (6) 96
Alice Marcie Goodwin (6) 97
Grace Darcy (7) 97
Sally Brandon (6) 98
Ben Fenwick (6) 98
Dana Buendia (6) 99
Beth Riddler (6) 99
Duncan Miles (6) 100
Elliot Clark (6) 100
Holly Watson (6) 101
Ben Atkinson (6) 101
Emily Cooke (6) 102
Charlotte Pointon (6) 102
Molly Craig (6) 103
Daniel Borg (7) 103
Christian Emmerson (6) 104
Charlotte Goulding (6) 104
Anna Silvie Reay (7) 105

Wingate Infant School, Wingate

Luke Coverdale (6) 105
Jasmin Clark (6) 106
Lewis Dixon (6) 106
Caine Cassidy (6) 107
Finley Curwen (6) 107
Leila Presho (5) 107
Daniel Setterfield (7) 108
Emma Robyn Blackett (5) 108
Georgia Vasey (6) 109
Zara Kate Williams (6) 109
Lily Belinda Gibson (6) 110
James Anderson (6) 110
Chloe Robins (5) 110

The Poems

Lee

L oves chocolate
E specially Kinder
E ggs

B est at bowling
R uns fast
O ften plays on the DS
W hen at home
N ever naughty.

Lee Brown (6)
Amble Links First School, Amble Morpeth

Brandon

B randon is
R eally kind
A lways happy
N ever sad
D oes run fast
O ften smiles
N ever naughty.

Brandon Thompson (5)
Amble Links First School, Amble Morpeth

Georgia

Georgia likes chocolate
Eats ice cream
Often happy
Remembers stuff
Great friend
Is always good
Always kind.

Georgia Schroeder (6)
Amble Links First School, Amble Morpeth

Michael

Michael
Is sporty
Can run fast
Has lots of energy
Always happy
Especially at Christmas
Loves presents.

Michael Alan Brown (6)
Amble Links First School, Amble Morpeth

Ella

Ella is beautiful
Loves to play with friends
Likes to play on her DS
Always good.

Ella Henderson (6)
Amble Links First School, Amble Morpeth

Charlie

C harlie is nice
H as a lovely smile
A lways happy
R eally clever
L ikes chocolate
I s friendly
E veryone likes Charlie.

Charlie Yates (6)
Amble Links First School, Amble Morpeth

Joanne

J oanne is
O ften smiling
A lways happy
N ever sad
N ever naughty
E veryone likes her.

Joanne Dawson (5)
Amble Links First School, Amble Morpeth

Shane

S hane is shy
H elpful
A lways funny
N ever cheeky
E specially good at making models.

Shane Nelson-Henderson (6)
Amble Links First School, Amble Morpeth

K ieran
I s good
E ats sweets
R uns fast
A lways plays
N ever is naughty.

Kieran Hume (6)
Amble Links First School, Amble Morpeth

Nathan

N athan is friendly
A lways cute
T ickly
H appy Nathan
A lways smiling
N ever sad.

Nathan Charlton (7)
Amble Links First School, Amble Morpeth

Shuana

S hauna is
H appy
A ll the time
U ses lots of energy
N ever sad
A lways smiling.

Shauna Carruthers (7)
Amble Links First School, Amble Morpeth

Tyler

Tyler is
Your best friend
Lovely boy
Everyone likes Tyler
Remember Tyler.

Tyler Charlton (5)
Amble Links First School, Amble Morpeth

Neeve

Neeve is
Everyone's best friend
Eats chips with tomato sauce
Very happy
Especially on her birthday.

Neeve Jamieson (6)
Amble Links First School, Amble Morpeth

Bobby

Bobby
Often runs in races
Best at sprinting
Best at running fast
Your best friend.

Bobby Stone (5)
Amble Links First School, Amble Morpeth

Lewis

Lewis loves
Eating chocolate
Wears nice clothes
Is always kind
Sometimes naughty.

Lewis Fairbairn (6)
Amble Links First School, Amble Morpeth

Emily

Especially good
Might be good
Impressive
Loves eating
Your best friend.

Emily Fairbairn (6)
Amble Links First School, Amble Morpeth

Adam

Adam likes chocolate
Does jobs too much
Adam loves playing on his DS
Might help people.

Adam Moyle (6)
Amble Links First School, Amble Morpeth

Sian

Silly Sian
Is always laughing
Always loves sweets
Never stops smiling.

Sian Moyle (6)
Amble Links First School, Amble Morpeth

Evan

Evan is
Very good
Always does as he is told
Never naughty.

Evan Jukes (5)
Amble Links First School, Amble Morpeth

Conor Doran

Conor likes running
Our school is great
Nobody likes wasps
Our teachers are great
Rabbits are cool

Do my best at my work
Often I play out
Rabbits are cool
Ants are great
Nets are wet.

Conor Doran (6)
Barlows Primary School, Liverpool

Emily Brooksbank

E veryone thinks I am lovely
M y friends are Zoe, Mia, Ella, Lucy and Maya
I like my mum and dad
L iteracy is fun
Y ou always play with me

B est at art
R eally likes chocolate
O n Sunday I go to church
O n Saturday I go to dance
K etchup is nice on chips
S piders are bugs
B ees can fly and sting
A nd I love maths
N ever ate cottage pie
K now lots about Italy.

Emily Brooksbank (6)
Barlows Primary School, Liverpool

Sam Cass

S am likes numeracy
A shleigh is Sam's best friend
M ichael is my brother

C ake is nice
A ndrew is my middle name
S am loves 2F
S am likes Hallowe'en.

Sam Cass (6)
Barlows Primary School, Liverpool

Harry Brierley

Harry is funny
And often I play out
Ready to go to school
Really like to play out
Yes, I use my Xbox 360

Be my best friend
Running to school
I like coming to school
Every day I do my homework
Reading books
Like watching television
Eat turkey
Yummy breakfast.

Harry Brierley (6)
Barlows Primary School, Liverpool

Maya Jones

Meeting new friends is exciting
And I don't like beetles
You are always nice to me
A friend like Emily

Joe is my favourite cousin
Only my friends can come to my party
Never eats chocolate
Everyone is my friend
Sleeps at ten o'clock.

Maya Jones (6)
Barlows Primary School, Liverpool

Lives in Barlows Lane
Us, we are friends
Chatty and funny
You love me

Best friends are Maya, Emily, Ashleigh, Mia and Zoe
Every day I learn
And I am good at geography
Useless at tennis
My favourite food is hot dogs
On Saturdays I go to LIPA
Never stops dancing
Tennis is horrible.

Lucy Beaumont (6)
Barlows Primary School, Liverpool

Ben Bentley

Ben is funny
Every day I go to school
Never forget to kiss my dad

Ben leaves for playschool
Every day I see my mum and dad
Never forget to kiss my mum and dad
Tidy my room
Lay my bed covers
Every day I watch the television
Yes is my favourite word.

Ben Bentley (6)
Barlows Primary School, Liverpool

Mia Wheeler

My mum and dad are nice
I am nice
Art is the best thing

Watch the telly with my grandad
Have eleven best friends
Everyone is my friend
Everyone thinks I am pretty
Like cucumber with salt and vinegar
England is the best
Really good at ICT.

Mia Wheeler (6)
Barlows Primary School, Liverpool

Jak Lydiate

Juicy apples are my favourite
And oranges I like too
Kick the football

Likes to go to the football
Year 2 is my class
Ducks swim in the pond
I like maths
And PE
Trucks are good
Easter is my favourite time.

Jak Lydiate (6)
Barlows Primary School, Liverpool

Ella Conway

Emily is my best friend
Literacy is fun
Loves everyone
Art is what I love

Chatty
On Saturday night or Sunday I go to church
Never bully
Watch TV every weekend
Always follow instructions
You are good at spelling words.

Ella Conway (6)
Barlows Primary School, Liverpool

Emma Jones

Everyone is friendly
My friends are Emily, Zoe, Maya, Lucy and Ava
My friends are funny
Amy is silly

Jelly is my favourite
On Sundays and Tuesdays I go to swimming
Never eat cottage pie
Everyone is nice
Spiders are scary.

Emma Jones (6)
Barlows Primary School, Liverpool

Eva Warbis

Every day I try my best
Very good at work
Always playing with Molly

What time shall I go to bed?
And I learn new things
Really good at eating
Being good at doing jobs
I like going swimming
So cool at singing.

Eva Warbis (6)
Barlows Primary School, Liverpool

Matthew

Makes lots of mess
At playtime I have fun
Terrific family
Tons of friends
Has lots of footballs
Enters lots of competitions
Wins trophies.

Matthew McDonald (6)
Barlows Primary School, Liverpool

Joshua

Jumps on the trampoline
Old car
Swimming
Helps his dad
Uses a phone
And I have a nap.

Joshua Bond-Readle (6)
Barlows Primary School, Liverpool

Oliwia

Often likes to play out
Lightly land when I jump
I am very good at horse riding
When I will have a dog
I will go on holiday to Scotland
An apple is too hard for me.

Oliwia Jankowska (6)
Barlows Primary School, Liverpool

Callum

Callum likes dancing
At the park I like to climb the trees
Listening to the teacher
Literacy is fun
Under the water when I go to swimming lessons
Molly's my friend.

Callum Walthew (6)
Barlows Primary School, Liverpool

Daniel

Daniel is my very own name
And I love playing outside
Never jumps in the deep end
I am brilliant on the computer
Eating chicken and curry
Loves Liverpool Football Club.

Daniel Grierson (6)
Barlows Primary School, Liverpool

Daniel

Daniel is a good footballer
At playtime we play
Never eats omelette
I like playing football
Everton is the best
Likes eating sausages.

Daniel Philip Snape (6)
Barlows Primary School, Liverpool

Joshua

Jumping is fun
Orange juice is yummy
Sausages are my favourite
Have a nice family
Under the bed I have toys
Apples are yummy.

Joshua Clark Newsome (6)
Barlows Primary School, Liverpool

Nicola

Nicola is funny and kind
I learn nearly every day in school
Clothes I wear, I like them
Over the bridge, I like the bridge
Love playing with my friends
All my friends are the best.

Nicola Ravenscroft (6)
Barlows Primary School, Liverpool

Lewis

Loves swimming
Eats chocolate
Waits for the train
I like my Thomas Train
Sings Spider-Man.

Lewis Doran (6)
Barlows Primary School, Liverpool

Megan

Megan loves Mum so much
Eat food at eight o'clock
Go outside to play
And I like playing games
Never goes near spiders.

Megan Dickson (6)
Barlows Primary School, Liverpool

Grace

Giggling all day long
Ready to play a game
And I like to play with my dolls
Creating a picture with paint
Eating pizza with cheese on top.

Grace Faulkner (5)
Barlows Primary School, Liverpool

Molly

My favourite friends are Eva and Halle
Octopuses are great
Loves listening to her teacher
Likes her friends for who they are
Yummy cakes.

Molly Garside (6)
Barlows Primary School, Liverpool

Luke

Laughing and loud
Utterly brilliant at handstands
Keeps his toys in the toy cupboard
Every day I tidy my bedroom.

Luke Evans (6)
Barlows Primary School, Liverpool

Solomon

S uper
O utstanding
L ovely
O riginal
M arvellous
O range
N ice

O utstanding
W inner
U nderstanding
S cience
U nbelievable.

Solomon Asante-Owusu (6)
Bowker Vale Primary School, Crumpsall

Momina Butt

M agical
O utstanding
M arvellous
I nnocent
N ice
A dorable

B eautiful
U nderstanding
T errific
T remendous.

Momina Butt (7)
Bowker Vale Primary School, Crumpsall

Humariaa Butt

H elpful
U nbelievable
M agnificent
A rtistic
R eminder
I nvestigative
A dorable
A dventurous

B eautiful
U nderstanding
T alented
T remendous.

Humariaa Butt (6)
Bowker Vale Primary School, Crumpsall

Megyn

M agical
E xciting
G ood
Y oung
N ice

L ovely
E xcellent
O utstanding
N ight.

Megyn Betty Leon (6)
Bowker Vale Primary School, Crumpsall

Akashraj

A rtistic
K ind
A dorable
S uper
H elpful
R ight
A dventurous
J olly.

Akashraj Singh (6)
Bowker Vale Primary School, Crumpsall

Sana Kayani

S uper
A rtistic
N ice
A dventurous.

Sana Kayani (6)
Bowker Vale Primary School, Crumpsall

Sami

S cience
A rty
M aking
I nstrument.

Sami Ahmad (6)
Bowker Vale Primary School, Crumpsall

Charlie

Charlie is crazy
Happy
Always eating chocolate
Really good at rugby
Likes strawberries
Is a good friend
Excited about going to my dad's house.

Charlie Cox (6)
Cambois First School, Cambois

Billie

Billie is beautiful
I like ice cream
Love my brother, Stevie
Loves cheerleading
I love my mommy
Every day I do breakfast club.

Billie Law (6)
Cambois First School, Cambois

Jacob

Jacob is very good at art
Art is fantastic
Caring
On Friday eats ice cream
Bake with Mum.

Jacob-Russan Pritchett (6)
Cambois First School, Cambois

Jennie

J umps high on the trampoline
E verybody likes her
N ever grumpy
N ever sleeps on the floor
I like playing hide-and-seek
E lephants are my favourite animals.

Jennie Butcher (6)
Cambois First School, Cambois

Kieran

K ieran is funny
I love doing my homework
E ats eggs
R eally good at listening to the teacher
A lways smiling
N ever ever naughty.

Kieran Elliott (6)
Cambois First School, Cambois

Stars

S hiny jewels
T iny dots
A round the world
R acing in the night
S himmering light.

Ruben Baron (6)
Castle Park School, Kendal

Nocturnal Animals

Normal animals are
Opening their eyes
Clawing animals
Turning around
Under bridges
Rolling around and jumping
Now animals are racing
Around so smile, so
Laugh and be nice in the night

A monster might bite
Now be careful right now
I might bite back
Maybe I might not bite
A frog might jump
Late at night
So be careful.

Daisy Schwarzer (6)
Castle Park School, Kendal

Stars

Stars are beautiful
To see on dark nights
At night the stars keep the dark light
Really stars are beautiful
See tonight.

Luke Tamblin (6)
Castle Park School, Kendal

Bedtime Stories

B rown moon rocks floating in the sky
E verybody asleep
D addy tucked me into my cosy bed
'T ime for bed,' said Mum
I am cosy and warm
M aking new beginnings
E verywhere

S tars glitter in the dark
T hrough my bedroom window
O nly me
R ainbows try to break through
I nteresting patterns
E veryone stares
S tars glitter through my window against the dark sky.

Paige Hogg (6)
Castle Park School, Kendal

The Moon

T he moon is glittering
H e is asleep
E verywhere is glittering

M oon is asleep
O cean is black
O ur beds are still
N ight-night.

Jessika Foulds (6)
Castle Park School, Kendal

The Bedtime Stories

Bedtime stories
Everyone lived happily
Dreaming nice dreams
Trying to sleep
In a cosy bed
Magic stories at night
Everybody is in bed

Some night I will see a star
Travelling high in the sky
Over mountains
Rolling rivers
I am fast asleep
Enjoying my dream
Stories for another night.

Theo Alderson (6)
Castle Park School, Kendal

Bedtime

Big bubble bath
Eating cookies
Dark night sky
Twinkling stars
Inside my warm bedroom
Moon shines bright
Everyone is dreaming.

Leah Rylands (6)
Castle Park School, Kendal

Racing Rockets

Red rockets
Are racing to an island
Countdown
In five, four, three, two, one
Nice people come to
Greet them

Reaching high
Over and over again until
Cockerels wake them
Keeping them alert
Everyone
Trying to
Stop.

Matilda Hall (6)
Castle Park School, Kendal

Bedtime

Black is everywhere at night
Everything is creepy at sunset
Dark is everywhere
There's no light at daybreak
In the dark sky at night, there is no sun
Many people go to the moon
Everything is black at night.

Scott Wilkinson (6)
Castle Park School, Kendal

Racing Rockets

Red rocket
Around the world
Catching dreams
In every house
Nowhere to
Go, but

Round and round
Over rivers, through
Cities
Knocking on doors
Everywhere
Till
Sunset.

Mia Jones (6)
Castle Park School, Kendal

Stars

Shining in the night sky
There are some twinkling stars
Around the universe, round and
Round they go
So many times, over and over again.

Abbie Barwise (7)
Castle Park School, Kendal

Stars

Sparkly stars
Tiny in the dark sky
Around the planet
Rain down like sparklers
Shiny stars.

Kyle Needham (6)
Castle Park School, Kendal

Stars

Stars are twinkly and bright
The nights are dark
And they give us light
Red stars
Sparkly and white.

Cody Haines (6)
Castle Park School, Kendal

Stars

Stars are big
Tumbling around in the sky
A bright orange light
Round in the night
Sparkly star.

Fraser Owen Donaldson (6)
Castle Park School, Kendal

Stars

Sharp, spiky stars
The golden stars
A shooting star
Red-hot in the night
Sparkly and bright.

Jacob Dixon (6)
Castle Park School, Kendal

The Stars

Small
The stars are bright and beautiful
Around the night sky
Racing to Mars
Shooting everywhere!

Nathaniel Key (6)
Castle Park School, Kendal

The Stars

Stars are bright
The stars are gold
Are pointy
Really high
Some come out at night.

Andrew Kneale (6)
Castle Park School, Kendal

Stars

Stars are beautiful
The stars always light up
A star comes out at night
Rabbits are asleep
Sparkling bright.

Dylan Beagan (6)
Castle Park School, Kendal

Stars

Stars shining in the night
Twinkle in the sky
Above the clouds
Round and round
Sparkling bright.

Scott James Darnborough (6)
Castle Park School, Kendal

Stars

Sparkly star
Twinkling bright
All through the night
Round in the sky
Stars are bright.

Jack Rigg (6)
Castle Park School, Kendal

Sparkling Stars

S tars are massive
T all in the sky
A bove the clouds
R eally bright
S parkly lights.

Rhys Wright (6)
Castle Park School, Kendal

Stars

S tars are really bright
T he yellow stars
A star is a twinkling light
R ed and shining star
S hooting stars in the night.

Alfie Burrow (6)
Castle Park School, Kendal

Stars

S parkling star I see tonight
T winkling and turning
A bove the clouds the stars are playing
R ed star that glows in the night
S tarlight, star bright, the golden star that sparkles in the night.

Sophie Kissock (6)
Castle Park School, Kendal

Stars

S tars are bright in the dark sky
T winkling stars spinning in the sky
A nd bright stars
R iding stars, twinkly stars
S parkling stars.

Ellie Kennah (6)
Castle Park School, Kendal

Star Poem

S parkly star
T winkling and turning
A bove the clouds so high in the sky
R ed stars are hot, really, really hot
S himmering in the sky.

Connor Jackson (6)
Castle Park School, Kendal

Stars

S tars are bright
T winkling in my eyes
A nother star lies beside
R ising sun is really hot
S tars shimmering in the sky.

Zachary Canwell (6)
Castle Park School, Kendal

The Moon

Moon comes out at night
Over the world
Over the town
Night-time light.

Denis Morar (6)
Castle Park School, Kendal

The Moon

Moon is like a stone
Over the Earth like a ball
Over the night sky
Never loses its light.

Lauren Slater (6)
Castle Park School, Kendal

The Moon

Moon shines
Over the dark night
Over the whole world
Never stops, just keeps moving.

Ryan Blayney (6)
Castle Park School, Kendal

The Moon

M oon
O ver the world
O range glows down
N ever stops, just keeps moving.

Alex Bland (6)
Castle Park School, Kendal

Stars

S ilvery star I see tonight
T winkling and turning
A bove the clouds, the stars sleep tonight
R ed star.

Nicole Leadbitter (6)
Castle Park School, Kendal

Green

G orgeous green apples
R eally sweet pears
E xciting green leaves
E ating green grapes
N oisy green Scouts going home.

Millie Wilson (7)
Christ Church Primary School, Wirral

Green

Green, lovely, juicy apples
Ripe green grapes
Exciting green cakes are gorgeous
Exciting, green, juicy apples
Now shops sell a lot of green peas.

Ellie Boultbee (6)
Christ Church Primary School, Wirral

Blue

Blueberries are gorgeous
Lewis has a blue Everton shirt
Unhappy underwater fish
Everyone's eyes are blue.

Kiera Payne (6)
Christ Church Primary School, Wirral

Red

Red roses are pretty
Everyone eats red strawberries
Dragons blow fire.

Chloe Hayward (6)
Christ Church Primary School, Wirral

Red

Red roses smell nice
Everyone eats lovely strawberries
Daddy wears red shoes.

Katie Taylor (6)
Christ Church Primary School, Wirral

Autumn

Above, leaves come down
Underneath are leaves
Trees' leaves are changing
Up, up in the trees, squirrels are hiding
Misty Mondays
Nuts are coming off.

Ben Weston
Ghyllside Primary School, Kendal

Autumn

Autumn is coming
Umbrellas might be needed
Time to get cosy
Under the trees there might be berries
Misty Mondays
Nuts fall off the trees.

Isla Norman (6)
Ghyllside Primary School, Kendal

Autumn

Apples falling
Usually cold
Time for Hallowe'en
Under the ground are little seeds
Mist in the distance
Nights are longer, days are shorter.

Angus Corrie
Ghyllside Primary School, Kendal

Autumn

Apples are falling
Up above, birds are getting ready to go
Time for hibernating
Unique toffee apples
Misty Mondays are coming
Nights are getting longer.

Grace Anastasie Cooke (6)
Ghyllside Primary School, Kendal

Autumn

Apples falling
Usually it's cold
Time for Hallowe'en
Unexpectedly the swallows come
Misty Mondays
Nights are getting longer.

Daniel Betoin
Ghyllside Primary School, Kendal

Autumn

A pples ready to eat
U nder the ground animals go to hibernate
T ime for eco council
U mbrellas may be used
M ornings get darker
N ights get longer.

Dylan Hill (6)
Ghyllside Primary School, Kendal

Autumn

A pples falling off the trees
U ntidy forests
T rees are getting bare
U ntidy leaves in a heap in the forest
M ists are forming
N asty smell of leaves.

Kate Slater (7)
Ghyllside Primary School, Kendal

Autumn

A ll the leaves are changing
U mbrellas might be needed
T ime to play outside with the leaves
U ntidy woods
M ight go out for walks in the woods
N asty winds or weather.

Phoebe Rudd (6)
Ghyllside Primary School, Kendal

Autumn

Above, leaves are changing
Up in the trees, leaves are falling
Things are falling down
Under, things are changing
Mothers come out to play
Now it is Hallowe'en, hooray!

Elizabeth Johnson
Ghyllside Primary School, Kendal

Autumn

Animals start hibernating
Under the trees you may see some ants
Trees get cold
Unfortunately we don't get butterflies
Maybe we should go to Hallowe'en discos and Bonfire Night
Now let's go outside.

Lucy Greener (6)
Ghyllside Primary School, Kendal

Autumn

Apples are falling
Umbrellas might be helpful
Trees are naked
Umbrellas might be wet at the end
Mmm, yummy food
Nights are cold.

Josh Smith (7)
Ghyllside Primary School, Kendal

Caitlin Whitehead

Cheeky
Amazing
Interesting
Tired
Lovely
Is a superstar
Neat at writing

Wonderful
Helpful
Is brill
Taught
Especially great
Hates writing
Exciting
Active
Don't like it when it is cold.

Caitlin Whitehead (7)
Heron Hill Primary School, Kendal

Sophie

So kind
Oh, so good
Popular
Helpful
Interesting
Excellent.

Sophie Butler
Heron Hill Primary School, Kendal

Xander Armstrong

Xander is fast
Amazing boy
Naughty sometimes
Does numbers on the computer
Eats quickly
Remembers stuff

Active child
Rough sometimes
Many toys
Smiley
Tall
Rich, a bit
Outside is good for him
Nervous sometimes
Goes to the Post Office a lot.

Xander Armstrong
Heron Hill Primary School, Kendal

Rebecca

Ruby-red lips
Excellent girl
Beautiful
Elegant
Colourful
Chatty
Awesome.

Rebecca Dyer
Heron Hill Primary School, Kendal

Lottie Beardwood

Lovely always
Oranges are my favourite fruit
Touching Lottie
Top Trumps is my favourite game
Ice cream is my favourite dairy thing
Excellent work I do sometimes

Big Ben is my favourite clock
Every day I go home from school with my friends
Any teeth that fall out, they come back
Radishes are my favourite vegetables
Doing things is my favourite thing
Wasting things I think is bad
Often honest
Often laugh
Doodling I love.

Lottie Beardwood
Heron Hill Primary School, Kendal

Michael

Makes cakes with Mum
Is gorgeous
Can climb up high
Has a trampoline
Always plays with his toys
Eats chips
Loves his mummy.

Michael Wilson
Heron Hill Primary School, Kendal

Gabriella Parker

G orgeous Gabriella
A lways kind
B rilliant with work
R eally sensible
I like to play with new friends
E at my food delicately
L ovely me
L ike pink and purple
A very nice person

P erfect lady
A lways helpful
R eally good
K ind and helpful
E at pancakes
R eady for my tea.

Gabriella Parker
Heron Hill Primary School, Kendal

Hannah

H as green eyes
A lways laughs
N ever gets sad
N ever gets angry
A lways smiles
H as golden hair.

Hannah Elvey
Heron Hill Primary School, Kendal

Caitlin Coombes

C an play with everybody
A lways likes reading
I like the telly
T ries to help
L ikes people
I remember everything
N eat at colouring

C aitlin's best friend is Tia
O ften play with new friends
O h, I sometimes help Mummy at home
M ake people laugh
B rillaint, daring
E at pancakes
S ay nice things.

Caitlin Coombes
Heron Hill Primary School, Kendal

Tia Foley

T ickly Tia
I ce cream is nice
A re you amazing?

F antastic Foley
O ften play with Caitlin W
L ucky Tia
E specially nice
Y ellow is my favourite colour.

Tia Foley (6)
Heron Hill Primary School, Kendal

Maddy Tidman

M arvellous at maths
A mazing work
D efinitely quick
D on't like bananas
Y ellow is my second favourite colour

T hinks very slowly
I s good at ICT
D id lots of guided reading today
M usical Maddy
A lways active
N ever noisy.

Maddy Tidman (6)
Heron Hill Primary School, Kendal

Isabel Toms

I s very kind
S he is a star
A lways good
B eautiful she is
E xcellent Izy
L aughing is good fun

T ries her best
O ne fab writer
M agic Isabel
S he always smiles.

Isabel Toms
Heron Hill Primary School, Kendal

Hallowe'en

Hallowe'en nights are dark and gloomy
All children scaring adults
Lots of vampires creeping about
Lots of naughty devils breathing very hot fire
On the scary table a scary pumpkin
White ghosts all around the house
Eek! Witch mixing her potions together
Elves are all so dressed up
Numeracy work you have to do after Hallowe'en.

Sam Jones (6)
Heron Hill Primary School, Kendal

Hallowe'en

Happy Hallowe'en
Adults afraid of ghosts
Lots of children dressing up
Lovely scary costumes to wear
On the dinner table there are pumpkins
Wet night on this Hallowe'en
Excellent
Everyone has fun
Near a house I said, 'Trick or treat!'

Joshua Irving (6)
Heron Hill Primary School, Kendal

Hallowe'en

H appy Hallowe'en is scary
A ll the children running around
L ots of pumpkins on the table
L oopy decorations
O wls hooting
W indows rattling
E verybody scaring other people
E veryone having fun
N aughty children scaring adults!

Amy Woodhouse (6)
Heron Hill Primary School, Kendal

Millie

M arvellous
I ncredible
L ovely
L ikely to play with someone else
I nteresting
E ntertaining.

Millie Stephens (6)
Heron Hill Primary School, Kendal

Tia

T an on my face
I nteresting
A wesome.

Tia Leather
Heron Hill Primary School, Kendal

Space

S tars are bright
P luto is the smallest planet
A stronauts are looking around
C omets are going around
E xploring.

Amy Dugdale (6)
Heron Hill Primary School, Kendal

Space

S parkly star
P lanets moving around the sun
A stronauts walk on the moon
C hildren like the planets
E agles falling down.

Louisa Dand (6)
Heron Hill Primary School, Kendal

Space

S am is in space
P eople went
A n alien is eating an apple
C hloe hid in a crater
E llie saw an alien.

Chloe Nileh O'Connor (6)
Heron Hill Primary School, Kendal

Ellie

Excellent Ellie
Laughing, me laughing
Lovely girl
Is really kind
Everyone, I am everyone's friend.

Ellie May
Heron Hill Primary School, Kendal

Space

Stars zooming in and out of space
Persevering for aliens
Awesome astronauts going to the moon
Creepy stars looking from black holes
Earth is where we live.

Luey Machell (6)
Heron Hill Primary School, Kendal

Space

Spaceman
Please can you see any
Aliens on the moon?
Can you see anything on the moon?
Enormous rocks on the moon.

Mason Wilson (6)
Heron Hill Primary School, Kendal

Space

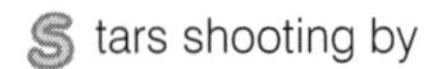

Stars shooting by
Planets big and small
Aliens gooey and slimy
Craters as big as Mars
Earth is where we live.

Danusia Pantechis (7)
Heron Hill Primary School, Kendal

Space

Stars shooting in space
Planets spinning around the sun
Aliens on the moon
Craters huge and dark
Earth is our planet.

Charlotte Dixon (7)
Heron Hill Primary School, Kendal

Calum

Cool
Amazing
Loves playing
Unbelievable
Musical.

Calum Morgan (6)
Heron Hill Primary School, Kendal

Miya

Makes lots of friends
Is always kind
Your best friend
Always helpful.

Miya Burrow
Heron Hill Primary School, Kendal

Marc

Mystical Marc
Amazing
Really nice
Cake is really nice.

Marc Milburn
Heron Hill Primary School, Kendal

Jake

Jake is a helpful
Active person
Kind at playing
Excellent at board games.

Jake Edwards (6)
Heron Hill Primary School, Kendal

Ben

B est at work

E ats pancakes

N ever gets angry.

Ben Mercer (6)
Heron Hill Primary School, Kendal

My Name Is Matthew

M ahem
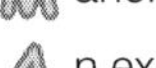
A n excellent tree climber
T he coolest boy

T he excellent skateboard rider
H appy
E ats chocolate
W e are cool

B ad
L azy
A nimal crazy
C laps his hands
K angaroos are my favourite animal
L onely
O ver-excited
C razy and mad
K icks footballs.

Matthew Blacklock (6)
Lamplugh CE School, Frizington

My Name Is Lizzie

Lovely
I am six years old
Zebras are my favourite animal
Zak is my friend
I like the colour red
Eleanor is my sister

Saville is my last name
Abby and Caris are my half-sisters
Verity is my cousin
I love my pets, especially my puppy
Laughs a lot
Lizzie is my name
Easter is my favourite.

Eleanor Saville (6)
Lamplugh CE School, Frizington

My Name Is Joe

Jolly Joe
O is a letter in my name
Eagles are my favourite kind of animal

Chatty
Used to be six
Stag beetles
Are my favourite kind of insect
Chocolate is my favourite kind of food
Kenzie is my best friend.

Joe Cusack (7)
Lamplugh CE School, Frizington

My Name Is Ben Shepherd

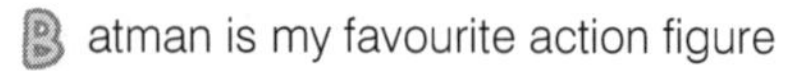

Batman is my favourite action figure
Every day I go on the Wii
Never bad

Six I am
Helpful
Eat pizza
Polite
Happy
Excellent at drawing
Runs fast
Dog is good and puppies too.

Ben Shepherd (6)
Lamplugh CE School, Frizington

My Name Is Bob

Bubblegum is my favourite gum
Only Grace is my sister
Bubbles are my favourite mixture

People like me
Racing is my favourite sport
Issey is my funny friend
Chris is my daddy
Eggs are my favourite lunch.

Bob Price (6)
Lamplugh CE School, Frizington

Seaside

S and
E xciting
A rmband
S ea
I ce cream
D eckchair
E njoy.

Sameer Munir (6)
Manchester Muslim Preparatory School, Withington

Seaside

S hell hunting
E ating fish
A nd chips
S unbathing and eating
I ce cream
D ogs playing
E xciting holiday.

Hannah Safiyya Awah (6)
Manchester Muslim Preparatory School, Withington

All About Me

U mbrella I have in the rain
M y mum likes to wash up
A pples are crunchy
R ed is my favourite colour.

Umar Jamaal Din (5)
Manchester Muslim Preparatory School, Withington

All About Me

H appy I feel when I see my grandad
A ngry I feel when my sister annoys me
S ad I feel when I fall down
A nxious when I meet someone new
N aughty I can be at times.

Hasan Bham (6)
Manchester Muslim Preparatory School, Withington

All About Me

A pples I like to eat
D are my friends to do things
L ittle baby animals are wild
A lways like to play on the computer
N eptune is my favourite planet.

Adlan Anazim (6)
Manchester Muslim Preparatory School, Withington

All About Me

I am five years old
S nakes are poisonous
A dlan is my best friend
A pples are crunchy
M um likes to cook food.

Isaam F Akhtar (6)
Manchester Muslim Preparatory School, Withington

Bradley

Bradley likes butterflies and lemons.
Reading is cool for him.
Apples are his favourite healthy food.
Destination makes him cool!
Learning is what makes him smart!
Every day he's being honest with his work!
Yellow is his best colour!

Casey Burton (6)
Mount Primary School, Wallasey

Dominic

Dominic is delicate because he is cut easily.
Odd Dom because he likes minibeasts.
Magnificent Dom because he climbed the climbing wall.
Intelligent Dom 'cause he does his work right.
Nice Dom because he does very nice things.
Interesting Dom because he does lots of science.
Cool Dom because he plays with his mates.

Dominic Bell (7)
Mount Primary School, Wallasey

Luke

Luke is likeable
Unbelievable Luke can write sentences
Kites are his favourite thing
Everyone likes to take pictures of him.

Freya Rivett (6)
Mount Primary School, Wallasey

Rebecca

Rocking Rebecca likes to play the guitar and the piano.
Excellent Rebecca does her work right.
Brilliant Rebecca made a rocking studio.
Excited Rebecca likes to listen to JLS 'Beat Again'.
Crazy Rebecca goes mad.
Cracking Rebecca cracks eggs.
Amazing Rebecca listens to Beyoncé's 'Sweet Dreams'.

Rebecca Anne Louise Stuffins (6)
Mount Primary School, Wallasey

Ronnie

Ronnie likes racing.
Orange is his favourite colour.
Noise is his beat.
'Nanny McPhee' is his best film.
Imagine, he loves to imagine.
Excited, he is excited.

Grace Myers (7)
Mount Primary School, Wallasey

Jack

Jack is great at jumping.
Amazing at running.
Clever at learning.
Keen at working.
James is Jack's favourite friend.

Heidi Slater (6)
Mount Primary School, Wallasey

Police

P eople go to jail.
O fficers
L ock them in jail.
I look for people.
C onstables.
E mergency 999.

Chloe Pybis Crowley (5)
Mount Primary School, Wallasey

Rachel

R achel has a little pet and games.
A nxious Rachel? No.
C ool Rachel because of her hair.
H istory, Rachel likes history.
E xciting Rachel can't wait till her birthday.
L ovely Rachel is pretty.

Rachel Foster (6)
Mount Primary School, Wallasey

Police

P olice arrest people.
O fficers sit in the police car.
L ock people up.
I put people in jail.
C ops run away.
E vidence day.

Emily Murray (6)
Mount Primary School, Wallasey

Katie

Kind Katie helps at school.
Angry Katie makes people angry.
Tired Katie went to bed.
Interesting Katie goes to the zoo.
Exciting Katie is amazing.

Katie Allen (6)
Mount Primary School, Wallasey

My Talking Partner

Aaron is amazing.
Aaron is an explorer.
Racing is not very nice for him.
On the carpet he sits very good.
Never is he silly.

Clara Satherley (6)
Mount Primary School, Wallasey

My Talking Partner

Lewis is a lovely person.
Egg is his favourite food.
William is his partner.
I like him.
School is his favourite thing.

William Joy (6)
Mount Primary School, Wallasey

Ellie

Ellie can't wait to go outside to play.
Lonely and loveable Ellie sits down on a rock.
Lovely Ellie cannot wait to go to school.
Intelligent Ellie wins the game again!
Exciting Ellie likes playing with her friends.

Ellie Jo-Anne Moore (6)
Mount Primary School, Wallasey

Phill

Phill is perfect at being smart and fantastic at being ready to learn.
He likes playing fab games outside.
Imaginative at imagining that he is in space.
Lovely at nearly everything.
Luke is his best mate.

Amy Dunderdale (6)
Mount Primary School, Wallasey

My Talking Partner

Casey likes cats and she is amazing at work.
Adventurous Casey is and she is small.
Sunshine is her best weather.
Everyone thinks Casey is cute.
Yellow is Casey's favourite colour.

Bradley Guy (6)
Mount Primary School, Wallasey

Luke

Lovely Luke likes to play
Usually Luke likes to play on the Nintendo Wii
Kind Luke likes to help others
Energetic Luke likes to bounce.

Luke Foulkes (7)
Mount Primary School, Wallasey

Owen

Owen is six years old.
Wild Owen is very wild.
Excellent Owen is a very excellent boy because he helps his mum.
Nice Owen is a very nice boy because he helps lots of people.

Owen Radcliffe (7)
Mount Primary School, Wallasey

Ben

Bouncy Ben bounces everywhere.
Excellent Ben jumps up and down.
Nice Ben plays with Fliss.

Ben Newton (6)
Mount Primary School, Wallasey

Austin

Addicted to footy.
Up at 7am every day.
Spain is my favourite place.
Team sports are the best
In the park every day.
Nice to my mum, because I love her.

Austin Mathison (7)
Parish CE Primary School, St Helens

Danny

Does everything as he is told.
Always uses his manners.
Never stops smiling.
Never stops chatting.
You would like him as a friend.

Danny Foster (7)
Parish CE Primary School, St Helens

Jack

Julie is my mum
Always playing football
Can score a goal
Keen on Manchester United
and I am keen on rugby.

Jack Martin (6)
Parish CE Primary School, St Helens

Tyreeze

Tyreeze is smart.
Yummy cakes for me.
Rain tickles me.
Elephants are bigger than me.
Eggs are yuck.
Zebras run faster than me.
Everybody is my friend.

Tyreeze Cunliffe (6)
St Edmund's RC Primary School, Manchester

Joseph

Joker on my mum
Oak trees are fun
Swinging for conkers
Emily is my friend and cousin
Playing football
Hair is blonde.

Joseph Mannion (6)
St Edmund's RC Primary School, Manchester

Nancy

Nancy loves school
Ahi is my friend and so is Breanna
Nancy loves dancing
Cerise used to be my friend
Yummy in my tummy.

Nancy Makaita Maziwisa (6)
St Edmund's RC Primary School, Manchester

Joseph

Jack is my friend.
Our school is the best.
Shannon is my sister.
Elephants are great.
People are kind.
Help the pandas.

Joseph Hegarty (6)
St Edmund's RC Primary School, Manchester

Emily

Elephants are loud
My hair is black and brown
I like eating sweets
Lions are scary
Yummy chips for tea.

Emily Crotty (6)
St Edmund's RC Primary School, Manchester

Katie

Katie is my name
Animals are my favourite
Tigers don't like me
I am a good friend
Eve is my friend.

Katie Heslop (6)
St Edmund's RC Primary School, Manchester

Abbie

A pples are good for you.

B abies are cute.

B abies laugh.

I love my family.

E lephants are big.

Abigail Jeffreys (6)
St Edmund's RC Primary School, Manchester

Imani

I like Miss Thompson

M y mother is so kind

A bbie is my best friend

N o, no we say to my baby cousin, Ryder

I like reading.

Imani Kolade-Newell (6)
St Edmund's RC Primary School, Manchester

Cade

C ousin to Breanna.

A handsome man.

D rawing good.

E veryone likes Cade.

Cade Serrette (6)
St Edmund's RC Primary School, Manchester

Josh

Joseph is my friend
Our school is great
Schools help you
Holy Lord.

Joshua Harris (7)
St Edmund's RC Primary School, Manchester

Jack

Jam to lick on a spoon
Always like to watch CBeebies
Crisps are yummy
Kimberley is my sister.

Jack Field (7)
St Edmund's RC Primary School, Manchester

All About Me

Zebra Zoe
Oranges
Eats eggs

Cute
Amazing
Racing
Tooth
Exploring
Roller skates.

Zoe Carter (6)
St Gregory's Catholic Primary School, Workington

All About Me

Hannah likes lollies.
Apple.
Nice.
Nuts.
Age 5.
Happy.

Roller skates.
Open the shop.
Snake.
Elephant.

Strawberries.
Matthew
Is kind.
Table.
Hannah raspberry.

Hannah Rose Smith (5)
St Gregory's Catholic Primary School, Workington

Conkers

Conkers tumbling
Orange leaves
Nuts falling
Kicking conkers
Everybody eating
Red leaves
Scarecrow.

Alfie McDonald (7)
St Gregory's Catholic Primary School, Workington

All About Me

Delicious
Exciting
Magic
Impressive
-
Lovely
Elegant
Explorer

Mine
Cute
Cuddly
Amazing
Nice
Noisy.

Demi-Lee McCann (5)
St Gregory's Catholic Primary School, Workington

Autumn

Conkers rolling
Oh no leaves on the hill
No leaves on the trees
Keep the conkers
Everyone playing
Red leaves on the trees
Soil growing plants.

Ashleigh Murphy (6)
St Gregory's Catholic Primary School, Workington

All About Me

Jessica likes Zoe.
Eats apples.
Soup.
Snakes like Jessica.
In Year 1.
Can jump.
All jumping.

Happy Jessica.
Under the Jessica.
Mum likes Jessica.
Eat up.
Strawberries.

Jessica Humes (5)
St Gregory's Catholic Primary School, Workington

Harvest Time

Hovering leaves
Around trees there's conkers
Rustling red leaves
Very cold allotment
Enormous trees
Swirling yellow leaves
Twinkly splats.

Jack Swinburne (6)
St Gregory's Catholic Primary School, Workington

Red Leaves

Rustling
Everywhere
Dropping

Leaves
Everybody
Apples
Very cold
Everybody
Swirling.

Kodie Kirkwood (6)
St Gregory's Catholic Primary School, Workington

Conkers

Colours
Orange
Nature
Kicking leaves
Everybody
Red
Swirling.

Ciaran O'Donnell (6)
St Gregory's Catholic Primary School, Workington

Conkers

Crunchy leaves
Orange, brown, red and yellow
Nearly winter
Keep snug and warm
Everywhere leaves
Rustling conkers
Swishing leaves.

Bailey Shaw (6)
St Gregory's Catholic Primary School, Workington

Conkers

Crunchy leaves
Orange, red and yellow leaves
Nearly winter
Keep snug and warm
Everywhere leaves are swirling
Rolling on the ground
Swirling, swishing around.

Lauren Bateman (6)
St Gregory's Catholic Primary School, Workington

Conkers

Crunchy leaves
Orange leaves
Nearly winter
Keep cleaning up
Everybody it's harvest time
Rain is falling
Spinning leaves.

Aimee Graham (6)
St Gregory's Catholic Primary School, Workington

Tumble Leaves Tumble

Tumbling leaves
Unusual trees
Muddy
Brown sticks
Long trees
Everybody is cold.

Josh Cunningham (6)
St Gregory's Catholic Primary School, Workington

All About Me

The girl
Ant
Yummy
Lovely
Aunty.

Tayla-Jaye Humphreys (5)
St Gregory's Catholic Primary School, Workington

All About Me

Cute
Outside
Running
Butterfly
Exciting
Nutter.

Corben Shaw (5)
St Gregory's Catholic Primary School, Workington

All About Me

Jolly
Oat
Super, splendid, smashing
Happy
Untidy
Amazing.

Joshua Lillico (5)
St Gregory's Catholic Primary School, Workington

Autumn

A falling leaf,
Conkers falling from the tree,
Orange, red and brown leaves,
Rustling hedgehogs in the leaves,
No creatures on the ground,
Spinning leaves rolling down.

Molly Davies (6)
St Gregory's Catholic Primary School, Workington

Gorilla

Grass is green.
On the top of his cage.
Rainforest.
In his cage.
Lip is big and strong.
Lap to drink.
Asleep, fast asleep.

Charlotte Anderson & Nattaliya Sehman (6)
St John's CE Primary School, Darlington

Tiger

The tiger is stripy
Intelligent and clever
Ginormous sharp claws
Extremely ferocious
Running and bounding.

Joshua Brannan (6)
St John's CE Primary School, Darlington

Lemur

Looks like a meerkat
Extra large grey and black tail
Mega sharp claws
Useful tail for climbing
Runs on the muddy floor.

Joel Towers (7)
St John's CE Primary School, Darlington

Snake

S limy slithery python.
N asty fangs.
A ttacks other animals.
K ills its prey.
E vil python.

Sam White (6)
St John's CE Primary School, Darlington

Snake

S lithery, slimy, sly snake
N asty, naughty
A ttack and squeeze
K ill by wrapping
E vil, poisonous boa constrictor.

Oliver Pattinson (6)
St John's CE Primary School, Darlington

Tiger

T errifying teeth
I n the jungle
G reedy, grabbing
E at eagerly
R oars ravenously.

Kayleigh Midgley (6)
St John's CE Primary School, Darlington

Frog

Fierce green frog.
Running rivers.
On a green lily pad.
Goggly eyes roll around.

Ellie White (6)
St John's CE Primary School, Darlington

Frog

Fat Mr Frog.
Rainforest.
Orange tongue.
Green poisonous frog.

Harry Doyle (6)
St John's CE Primary School, Darlington

Frog

Fat Mr Frog
Rainforest wet
On the frog was poison
Green.

Jack Wheelhouse (6)
St John's CE Primary School, Darlington

Frog

Frog, squashy frog.
Running on time.
On and on, jumping frog.
Green frog sitting on the forest floor.

Rebecca Hastie (6)
St John's CE Primary School, Darlington

Frog

Forest is dark and wet.
Rain drops down over the trees and crispy leaves.
Orange bumpy skin.
Green trees and green leaves.

Sinead Johnstone (6) & Demi-Lee Wilson (7)
St John's CE Primary School, Darlington

Frog

Fantastic frog runs
Rainforest
Outside are noises
Goggly huge eyes.

Chloe Sperring (6)
St John's CE Primary School, Darlington

Frog

F erocious, evil, squishy frog
R ough and bumpy skin
O pen red eyes blinking
G round; rough, hard and wet.

Holly Cowley (6)
St John's CE Primary School, Darlington

Frog

F orest is dark and wet.
R ain drips down over the trees.
O ranges growing in the trees.
G reen leaves in the trees.

Mia Wall (6)
St John's CE Primary School, Darlington

Frog

F ast frog in the
R ainforest
O range frog
G reen.

Matthew Plimmer (6)
St John's CE Primary School, Darlington

Autumn

Autumn is fun
Under the leaves I play
Times in autumn are cold
Up the tree the squirrels climb
My sister collects sticks
Night-time gets cold.

Emily Addison (5)
St Joseph's RC Primary School, Coundon

Autumn

Autumn is dark
Up in the trees there are wonderful red leaves
The forest is cold and windy
Using coloured leaves we made a pattern
My dog has fun in the leaves
New leaves fall every day.

Ruth Alderson (5)
St Joseph's RC Primary School, Coundon

Autumn

Autumn is beautiful
Under the leaves I find my friends
Time to eat my lunch
Up the trees I climb
My mum bakes cakes
Now I kick a football.

Laura Askew-Wells (5)
St Joseph's RC Primary School, Coundon

Autumn

Autumn has lots of leaves falling down
Up in the sky it is cold
The trees are beautiful
Up in the sky it is cloudy
Mam went to the forest
Nana went to the park.

Kai Wheatley (5)
St Joseph's RC Primary School, Coundon

Autumn

Autumn is beautiful
Under the trees are squirrels eating nice nuts
Trees are wonderful with different coloured leaves
Underneath the trees there are leaves
Mornings in autumn are cold
New leaves grow on the trees in spring.

Kerandeep Randhawa (5)
St Joseph's RC Primary School, Coundon

Autumn

Autumn leaves change colours
Under the trees are colourful leaves
Today it is autumn
Up in the tree there were some nuts
My sister collects acorns
Next morning it was cold.

Meera Marley (5)
St Joseph's RC Primary School, Coundon

Autumn

Autumn is fun.
Under the leaves animals play.
The leaves fall off the trees.
Using leaves for pictures.
Mam kicking leaves.
Night-time is chilly.

Alannah Burns (6)
St Joseph's RC Primary School, Coundon

Autumn

A leaf fell off the tree
Up in the trees there are pretty orange leaves
The crispy leaves are fun to play in
Under the trees the leaves are twirling
Me and Grandma went to the forest
Next time I will go to Hamsterley Forest.

Sam Bewick (5)
St Joseph's RC Primary School, Coundon

Autumn

Autumn days are mostly windy.
Umbrellas for the rain.
The leaves are blowing.
Up go the umbrellas.
Mum, can I go outside?
Now can we go home?

Elliott Barry (6)
St Michael's RC Primary School, Houghton-le-Spring

Playtime

P laying outside is fun
L et's play a game
A ll the children play outside
'Y ell, scream, shout,' we say
T ime to play tig
I love that game
M e and my friends are playing
E veryone is happy.

Connor James Lavelle (6)
St Michael's RC Primary School, Houghton-le-Spring

Playtime

P laying outside.
L aughing our heads off.
A ll of us playing.
Y ak, yak, yak, we're talking.
T ime for tea.
I 'm full.
M y friends are going home.
E *ee!* It's been a long day, goodnight!

Luke Sinton Robson (7)
St Michael's RC Primary School, Houghton-le-Spring

Playtime

P laying is fun.
L et's play lots of games.
A ll of the children are playing.
Y ells all about.
T ime to play another game.
I 'm exhausted.
M y friends are playing with me.
E nd of today.

Emma Bowater (6)
St Michael's RC Primary School, Houghton-le-Spring

Playtime

P laying on the bouncy hoppers
L et's go and play
A mazing fun and games
Y ell, shout when we play zombies
T hat was brilliant
I am having fun
M y friends have lots of games
E very day should be playtime.

Olivia Lish (6)
St Michael's RC Primary School, Houghton-le-Spring

Playtime

Playing football is fun
Let's play outside
Alan scored a goal!
Yells and shouts!
Time for fun
I think it's brill
Mister Foster rang the bell
Everyone froze.

Bradley McCarthy (6)
St Michael's RC Primary School, Houghton-le-Spring

Playtime

Playing in the sand.
Let's go to the beach.
All day to play.
Yells and shouts.
Time to go in.
I go back inside.
Mum comes to pick me up.
Everyone goes home.

May Turner (6)
St Michael's RC Primary School, Houghton-le-Spring

Playtime

Play in the sun
Let's go to the zoo
Animals to discover
You will have fun
Time for tea
I like playing out
Mam cooks lovely pasta
Everyone had fun.

Thomas Weetman (6)
St Michael's RC Primary School, Houghton-le-Spring

Playtime

Playing outside.
Let's go on the trampoline.
Andrew scored a goal.
You can play football now.
Time for tea.
I am having fun.
Mam cooked chicken nuggets and chips.
Everyone liked it.

Taylor Bowe (7)
St Michael's RC Primary School, Houghton-le-Spring

Playtime

Painting a picture
Love to play all day
A lovely day outside
Yells and shouts
The sun is shining
I jump on the bouncy hoppers
My game is better then yours
End the day with a smile.

Chloe Chapman (6)
St Michael's RC Primary School, Houghton-le-Spring

Seaside

Sea is fun.
Everyone loves the sea.
All of us are in the water.
Sun has come out.
I love the beach.
Dinner time, I am loving it.
Everyone loves the sea.

Isaac Lulham (6)
St Michael's RC Primary School, Houghton-le-Spring

Seaside

S ea is fun.
E ven the dog is here.
A ll the people in the sea are having fun.
S inging in the sea.
I am having fun.
D igging up the sand.
E njoy the day.

Harry John Huitson (6)
St Michael's RC Primary School, Houghton-le-Spring

Seaside

S ea is fun.
E veryone is having a good time.
A ll the time I see a fish.
S ometimes I see boats coming in.
I love the sand.
D inner - sandwiches, yum-yum.
E nd of day, it was great.

Bethany-Louise Burnhope (7)
St Michael's RC Primary School, Houghton-le-Spring

Autumn

Autumn days are fun.
Under the leaves are snails.
Try crunching leaves.
Usually it starts to rain heavily.
Misty and rainy and cloudy.
Now time for bed.

Venna Brumby (6)
St Michael's RC Primary School, Houghton-le-Spring

Autumn

Autumn is a cold season.
Under the trees there are leaves.
Try to sweep up the leaves.
Up goes your umbrella because it's raining.
Misty mornings are so miserable.
Now it's tea-time, I wonder what we're having.

Emily Robinson (6)
St Michael's RC Primary School, Houghton-le-Spring

Autumn

Autumn days are great fun
Under the trees there are some leaves
Time to sweep
Up and down the garden
My brush sweeps up all the leaves
Now I'm tired, goodnight!

Matthew Robinson (6)
St Michael's RC Primary School, Houghton-le-Spring

Autumn

Autumn days are unusual.
Up goes my umbrella.
Try to avoid very slippy leaves.
Usually I get my kite up.
Mum's sweeping up the leaves.
Now the rain's stopping.

Alexander Winter (7)
St Michael's RC Primary School, Houghton-le-Spring

Autumn

Autumn is a happy time.
Under the leaves are snails.
Try to not slip on the leaves.
Up above is my kite.
My hands are cold.
Now it is time for tea.

Charlie McLeod (6)
St Michael's RC Primary School, Houghton-le-Spring

Autumn

Autumn is a windy season.
Under the leaves hide the snails.
Time to look for bugs.
Up go all the umbrellas.
My mum is making tea.
Now it's time for tea.

Lily Masters (6)
St Michael's RC Primary School, Houghton-le-Spring

Party

P lay musical bumps
A ll the sausages taste good
R eally good dancing
T ime to blow candles
Y ou love eating cake.

Chloe Brice (6)
St Michael's RC Primary School, Houghton-le-Spring

Party

P lay musical statues.
A nnabelle is coming.
R ock, rock goes the music.
T ime for cake.
Y ell hooray!

Annabelle Napier (6)
St Michael's RC Primary School, Houghton-le-Spring

Party

P ark my car outside.
A ll my friends are coming.
R eally good music.
T ime to go home.
Y our birthday was good.

Sophia Robson (6)
St Michael's RC Primary School, Houghton-le-Spring

All About Me

Ellie is exciting
Lots of games I play
Likes to go to dancing
I love my little brother, Sam
Ella is my best friend

My birthday is in July
Animals are very cute
Carbonara is my favourite food
Cake is lush
I am very good at riding my bike
Oliver and Jake are my cousins
Carrots are crunchy
Can you jump as high as me?
'Harry Potter' is a great film
I love this poem.

Ellie Macciocchi (6)
Star of the Sea RC Primary School, Whitley Bay

William

Whizzy Will; I run so fast
I like to run on the beach
Love rugby
Love tennis
I am a sporty boy
And eat my spaghetti Bolognese
My muscles will grow big.

William Gray (6)
Star of the Sea RC Primary School, Whitley Bay

Mark Arquintillo

McDonald's is the best.
And I love spelling tests.
Riding my bike is what I like.
Karate is also my favourite fight.

And I like school.
Rubix Cube is so cool.
Queue is what I hate.
Uh! I don't really skate.
I like going to Whitley Bay.
November 1st is my birthday.
Tug of war is a fun game.
I see people throw litter, what a shame.
Love Mammy and Daddy.
Love sisters and brother.
Oh! I almost forgot my granny.

Mark Archer R Arquintillo (6)
Star of the Sea RC Primary School, Whitley Bay

Getting Around

My favourite toys are buses and trains.
A bus has four wheels.
Trains run on tracks.
The trees are losing their leaves.
Holidays are good for you.
Eating tomatoes is good for you.
Waves is the best swimming pool.

Matthew Duffy (7)
Star of the Sea RC Primary School, Whitley Bay

My Favourite Things

C arlo is my name
A eroplanes are my kind of game
R unways help the planes to take off
L ooking out of the aeroplane window
O h the people look like ants below

R eading is my next favourite thing
E very book I bring home I read
D inosaurs, an atlas and Dr Who are books I like
P laying with Lego is fun
A nd building cars, buses
T rains and tractors are what I like best
H elping my sister build Lego towers,
we can play for hours.

Carlo Redpath (6)
Star of the Sea RC Primary School, Whitley Bay

Ely Medina

E ly is my name
L oving daughter I am
Y ou'll like me if you get to know me

M e and my friends love to tell jokes
E very time we are together we always have fun
D ana is the name of one of my friends
I n school we learn lots of things
N ext when we're outside we play
A nd we share snacks and we share secrets together.

Ely S Medina (6)
Star of the Sea RC Primary School, Whitley Bay

It's All About Me!

Erin is six but as tall as eight
Running fast, she must not be late
I love my mummy
No one should believe in ghosts

Cows go moo
Anna is my best friend
Under the grass are creatures
Leaves are green
Freaky Friday
I like swimming
Eventually I will be seven
Lies are bad
Days are short in winter.

Erin Caulfield (6)
Star of the Sea RC Primary School, Whitley Bay

Favourite Things

My favourite animal is a kitten.
Orange is my favourite fruit.
Licking ice cream is yummy.
Lovely feelings in my tummy.
Yummy, yummy, yummy.

Running is my favourite sport.
Up and down the hills.
Dancing in the kitchen is fun.
Doing the moves with my mum.

Molly Rudd (6)
Star of the Sea RC Primary School, Whitley Bay

Josiel Martin

Joyful at all times
Offers help to anyone with a
Smile
In loving kindness.
Enthusiastic to
Learn everything.

Manages any situation without
Asking any questions.
Really great
To friends
In caring and
Never say no to the needy.

Josiel Martin (6)
Star of the Sea RC Primary School, Whitley Bay

Jude Raynor's World

Jude is my name.
Usually I am a good boy.
Down on the beach I like to play.
Every night I read to my mum or dad.

Reading is fun.
After school I like to see my brother.
Younger than me, he is four.
Nice boys like me will get treats.
Overnight I get my sleep,
Ready for a new day in the morning.

Jude Raynor (6)
Star of the Sea RC Primary School, Whitley Bay

All About Alice

Alice is six
Loves playing
In her favourite spot
Catches the ball
Every time

Good at numbers
Oh no, no
Oh no, no
Doing lots of sums
Winning games nearly all the time
In her garden
Near her school.

Alice Marcie Goodwin (6)
Star of the Sea RC Primary School, Whitley Bay

Grace Darcy

Great Grace is seven this year
Rachel is my big sister
After school I go to the swimming pool
Cats are cool
Ely is my friend from school

Daring things I like to do
And my favourite colour is blue
Running around is fun to do
Cheerfully I like to sing
Yay! Ponies are my favourite thing.

Grace Darcy (7)
Star of the Sea RC Primary School, Whitley Bay

Sally Brandon

S weet, special, a shining star
A lways smiling, singing songs
L oves to dance and join the fun
L oves to cuddle, dress-up and run
Y ellow hair

B eautiful brown eyes
R osy red cheeks
A doring child
N ever naughty
D oesn't cry
O ften shy
N early perfect, Sally, that is I.

Sally Brandon (6)
Star of the Sea RC Primary School, Whitley Bay

Ben's Wonderful World

B lue is a brilliant colour.
E lephants are big and noisy.
N o girls allowed in my room.

F ruit is good for us.
E ars are used for listening.
N oddy is my brother's favourite.
W ill is my best friend.
I love my keyboard.
C hocolate is a nice treat.
K eep my money safe.

Ben Fenwick (6)
Star of the Sea RC Primary School, Whitley Bay

Things I Know

Day after day I go to school.
After class I go outside to play.
Next I play racing with my friends.
All the time is fun.

Best friends stick together.
Understanding is needed.
Everybody is part of God's family.
No one forgets God.
Dancing is one of our talents.
'Ice Age' is one of my favourite movies.
Always pray to God.

Dana Buendia (6)
Star of the Sea RC Primary School, Whitley Bay

Beth's World

Beth likes flowers and rainbows
Eats cakes
The stars glitter in the sky
Hallowe'en is scary

Roses are pretty and lovely
Ice skating is fun
Daddy is lovely
Dandelions are yellow
Little Red Riding Hood is cute
Elephants are big
Red is my best colour.

Beth Riddler (6)
Star of the Sea RC Primary School, Whitley Bay

Duncan's Favourite Animals

Dolphins are wet
Unicorns don't exist
Newts make me nervous
Cats are in the family of tigers
Anteaters eat ants
Now for some more cool animals.

Mice are fast
Iguanas are lizards
Leopards have spots
Elephants are slow
Snakes have scales.

Duncan Miles (6)
Star of the Sea RC Primary School, Whitley Bay

All About Me

Everyone likes my curly hair
Laughs out loud and does not care
Lives in a village called New Hartley
Interested in everything that's fun
On my birthday I will be seven
Talks non-stop to Mum and Dad

Can ski down mountains in France
Love my black Labrador, Paddy
Always looks after his friends
Really enjoys eating fish and chips
Karate keeps me strong and fit.

Elliot Clark (6)
Star of the Sea RC Primary School, Whitley Bay

Holidays

Happy holidays
Out in the swimming pool
Lollies and ice cream; yum-yum
Laughing with my family
Yellow sun shining bright

Water keeps me cool
Alligator in the pool
Time to get out
S*plish, splash, splosh!*
Oops it popped, alligator gone
Never mind, you can buy another one.

Holly Watson (6)
Star of the Sea RC Primary School, Whitley Bay

Hallowe'en

Ben is bold
Even when told
Night of All Hallows

Apple bobbing
Trick or treating
Kind people giving
In the dark night
Not taking fright
Soon will be morning
Over it is
Next will be Christmas, can't wait.

Ben Atkinson (6)
Star of the Sea RC Primary School, Whitley Bay

Emily Likes Elephants

Emily likes elephants.
Mysterious animals.
I would like to kiss one.
Lovely big ears.
You could stroke one if you could reach.

Cheerful and happy elephants.
One little tail.
Outside they can squirt water.
Keep out when they are poorly.
Elephants are enormous.

Emily Cooke (6)
Star of the Sea RC Primary School, Whitley Bay

Charlotte P

Cheeky Charlotte can do
Handstands
And
Roly-poly's at home
Likes to play with her friend, Shruthi,
On
The
Tyres
Every breaktime at school.

Pink is Charlotte's favourite colour.

Charlotte Pointon (6)
Star of the Sea RC Primary School, Whitley Bay

Monkeys Like Eating

Monkeys are my favourite animal
Of them all
Lovely bananas they like to eat
Lots and lots
'Yum-yum,' says the monkey.

Climbs up the tree for another one
Reaches and stretches
And grabs it
Into his mouth
Gobbles it up!

Molly Craig (6)
Star of the Sea RC Primary School, Whitley Bay

Daniel Borg

Daring
Always good at school
Never does anything wrong
Ignores people when he should
Enjoys school
Loves maths

Builds models
Often plays the great Game of Britain
Reads a lot of books
Great writer.

Daniel Borg (7)
Star of the Sea RC Primary School, Whitley Bay

Christian

C hristian is cute
H elpful at home
R uns very fast
I nterested in skateboarding
S illy sometimes
T he best giggle
I like playing
A lways chilled
N ever nasty.

Christian Emmerson (6)
Star of the Sea RC Primary School, Whitley Bay

My Cousin Clare

C lare is my cousin
H er hair is shiny
A nd she has blue eyes
R obbie is my brother
L ike Clare and me he has blue eyes
O n Wednesday we often see her at Grandma's
T ogether with my sister Rhea
T eatime is great fun
E specially with Clare!

Charlotte Goulding (6)
Star of the Sea RC Primary School, Whitley Bay

Out In The Sun

A way, away, go away
N ow I want to go and play
N obody knows my secret game
A nna Banana is my name

R un, run out in the sun
E very day to have some fun
A n acrobat is what I'd like to be
Y ears of practice in front of me.

Anna Silvie Reay (7)
Star of the Sea RC Primary School, Whitley Bay

Rock Pool

R ocky, bumpy rock pool
O ctopus lying in the rock pool
C rabs in the rock pool
K icking stones over

P eople look for crabs
O ctagon
O val rocks
L obsters nip people in the rock pool.

Luke Coverdale (6)
Wingate Infant School, Wingate

Rock Pool

R ough rocks
O val rocks
C rashing rocks
K eep the water in

P eople looking for crabs in rocks
O ctagon rocks
O pened rocks
L obsters in the rock pool.

Jasmin Clark (6)
Wingate Infant School, Wingate

Dinosaur

D inosaurs eat people
I t is fierce
N eed to fight for meat
O n the beach dinosaurs roar
S ome dinosaurs eat grass, some eat leaves
A dinosaur can stand on you
U p in the sky a pterodactyl is there
R un from the dinosaur.

Lewis Dixon (6)
Wingate Infant School, Wingate

Shells

Shells are shiny
Hard and smooth
Eels are slooping and looping
Light shells
Luminous shells
Seaside shells.

Caine Cassidy (6)
Wingate Infant School, Wingate

Crabs

Crawling crabs
Running crabs
A racing crab
Big red crabs
Snipping crabs.

Finley Curwen (6)
Wingate Infant School, Wingate

Shiny

Slimy, shiny
Happy
Important
Nice, happy, gold
Yes I like gold.

Leila Presho (5)
Wingate Infant School, Wingate

Crabs

C olourful crabs
R acing crabs
A clever crab
B ig crabs are biting my toes
S ome crabs bite their food.

Daniel Setterfield (7)
Wingate Infant School, Wingate

Shiny

S hiny
H ot dust in the pocket
I n the fairy's pocket
N obody found the dust
Y ellow dust.

Emma Robyn Blackett (5)
Wingate Infant School, Wingate

Crabs

Crabs are orange
Red crabs
A crab has pointy nippers
Beautiful crabs
Snipping crabs.

Georgia Vasey (6)
Wingate Infant School, Wingate

Crabs

Crabs are orange
Running round in circles
Always snip people's toes
Big crabs
Some crabs' homes are shells.

Zara Kate Williams (6)
Wingate Infant School, Wingate

Sand

S hiny sand
A mazing sand
N ice silky sand
D rowned sand.

Lily Belinda Gibson (6)
Wingate Infant School, Wingate

Sand

S ilky soft sand
A mazing sand
N ear the sea there is wet sand
D rowned sand.

James Anderson (6)
Wingate Infant School, Wingate

Cat

C uddly cat
A lways purring
T he kitten likes milk.

Chloe Robins (5)
Wingate Infant School, Wingate